INCURABLY MAD!

by Sergio Aragones

Edited by Albert B. Feldstein

WARNER BOOKS

A Warner Communications Company

WARNER BOOKS EDITION

This Warner Books Edition is published by
arrangement with E.C. Publications, Inc.

Warner Books, Inc., 75 Rockefeller Plaza, New York, N.Y. 10019

A Warner Communications Company

Printed in the United States of America

First Printing: March, 1977

Reissued: September, 1985

10 9 8 7

To Nick Meglin

①

②

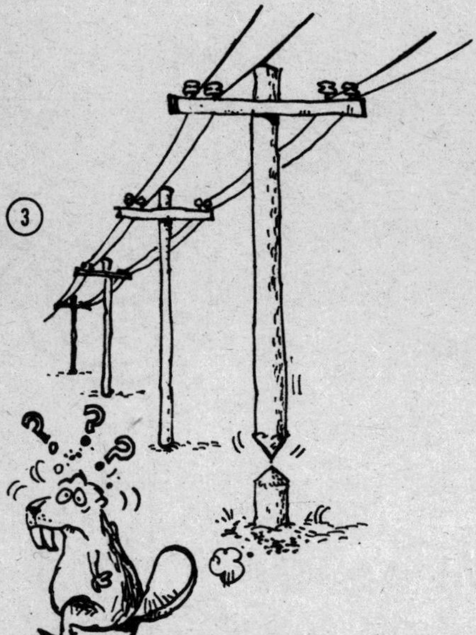
3

1
2
POOF!

3

1
2

(3)

L & W
97149

①

2

FOR SALE
FOR SALE
FOR SALE
FOR SALE
FOR SALE
FOR SALE
FOR SALE
FOR SALE
FOR SALE
FOR SALE
FOR SALE
FOR SALE
FOR SALE
FOR SALE
FOR SALE
FOR SALE
FOR SALE
FOR SALE
FOR SALE

1

2

3
SPLAT!

SCENE IV

①

②

3

1

2

(3)

MARIA

1

2

③

DOWN WITH AUTOMATION
THE GUILLOTINE UNFAIR TO EXECUTIONERS

1
2

3

(1)

(2)

PET
SHOP

1
CRASH!
2
BLAM!

3

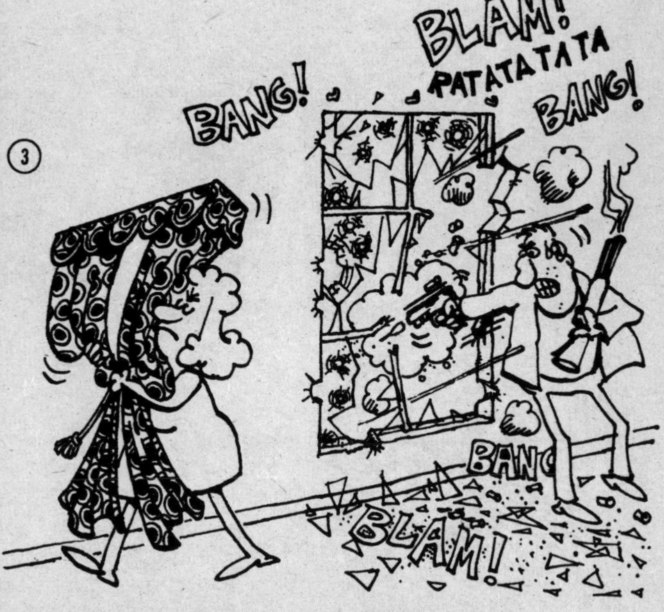
BANG!
BLAM!
PATATATATA
BANG!
BAN
BLAM!

1

2
WACK!

1
2

③

1
2

(3)

1
TELEP
2
KNOCK!
KNOCK!

3

ROLLER COASTER MFG. CO.

1
2

3

1
2

(3)

①

2

HOT

1
2

3
ZZZZ

1

2

3

①

②

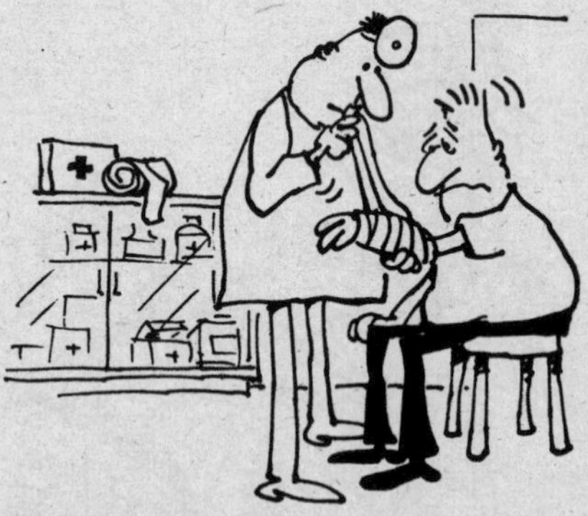

3

1

2

3

1

(2)

MUSEUM

1
2

3

1

2

3

①

2

1
TV
TV

2

1

2

③

①

②

(3)

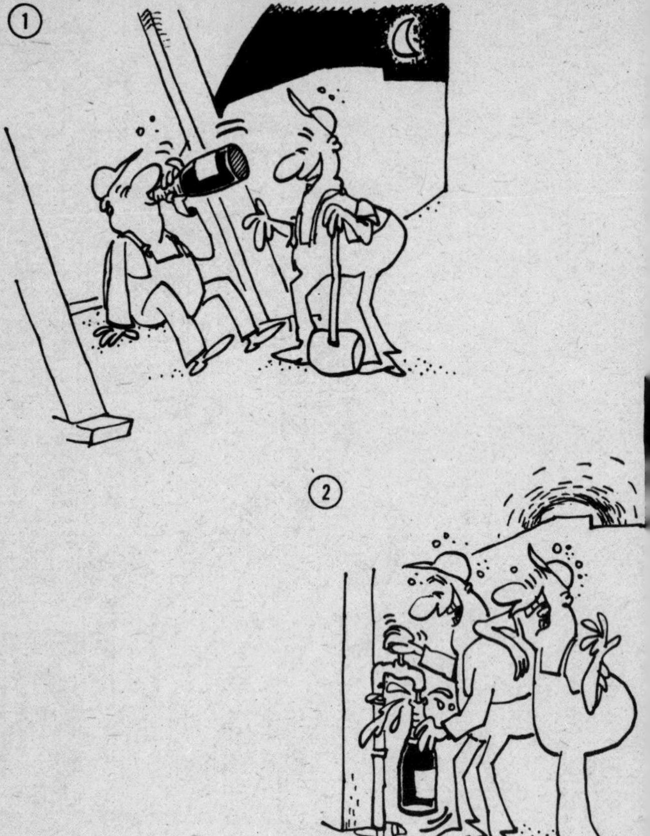
1
2

3

1
2

①

②

1

TOUR STA

VACANCY

①

(2)

1

2

NEW SITE
DE LUXE
TOWERS

1
JUST
MARRIED
2
JUST
MARRIED

3

1

2

FRUIT OF THE LOOM

703
201

1

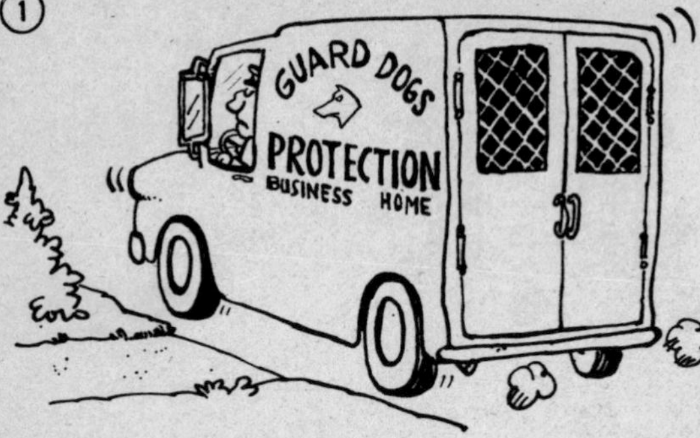
GUARD DOGS
PROTECTION
BUSINESS HOME

2

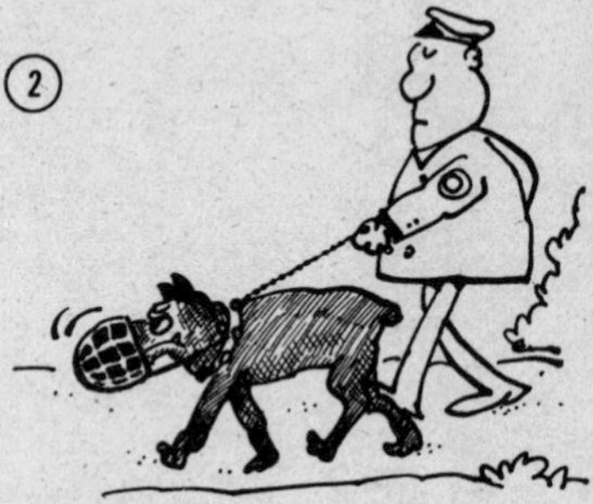

3

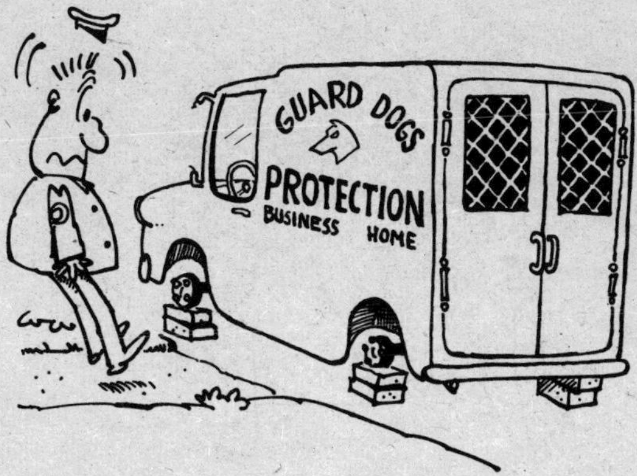
GUARD DOGS
PROTECTION
BUSINESS HOME

1

2

3

4

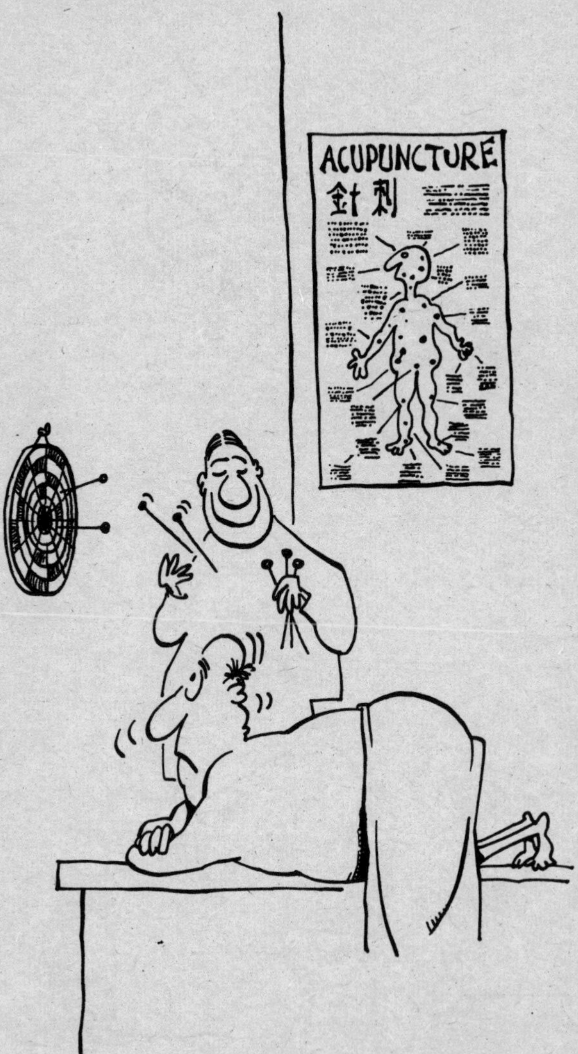
ACUPUNCTURE
針刺

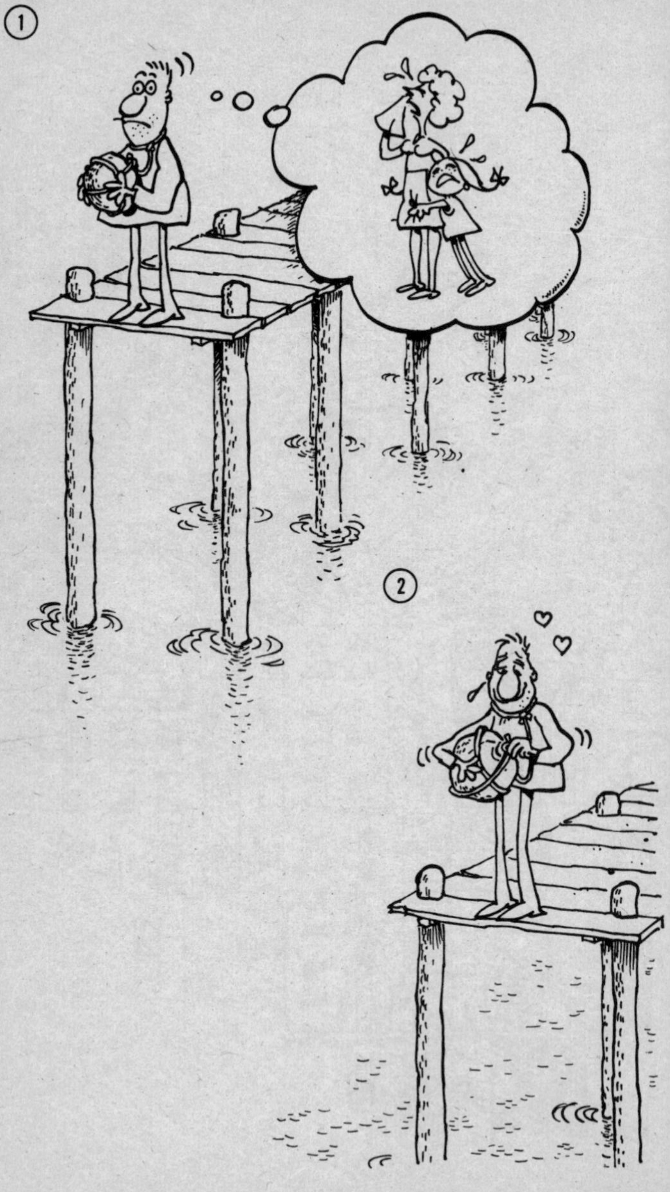
1
2

3

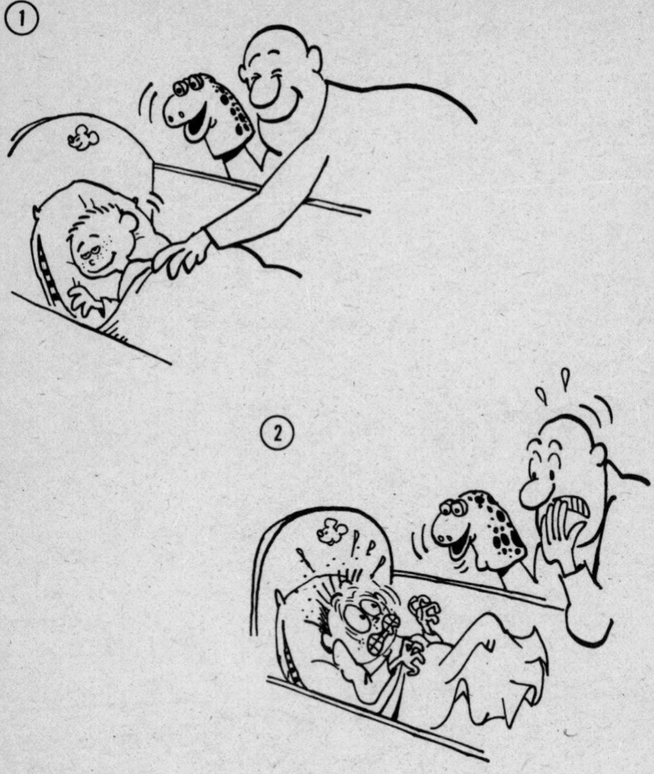

3

BIG
RACE
START

①

2

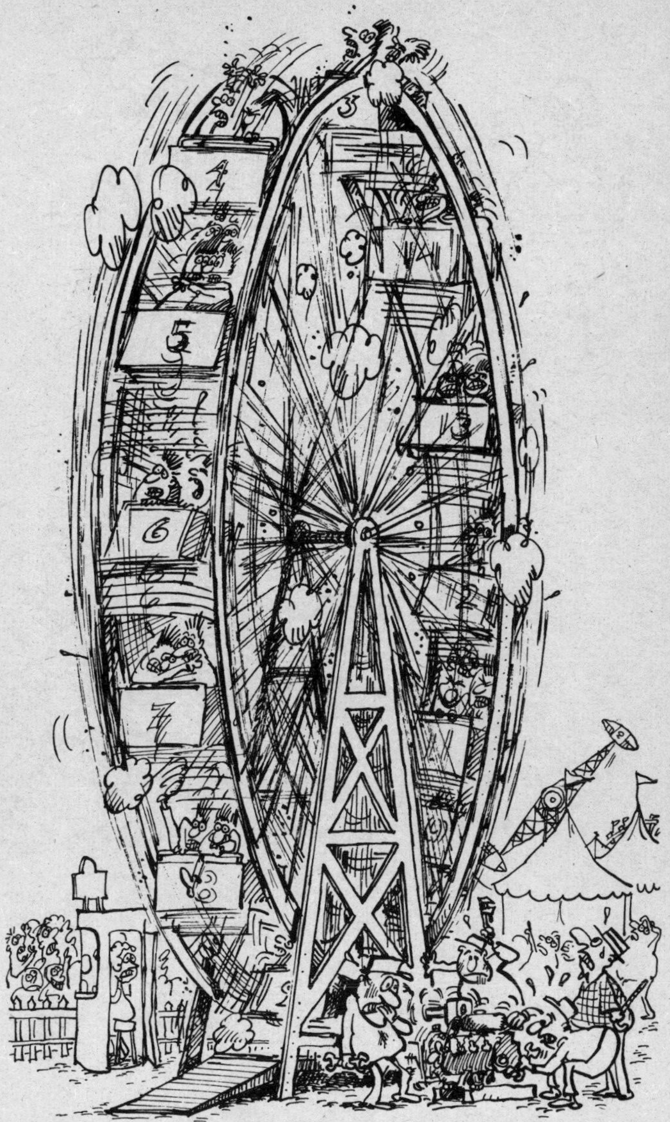

4
5
6
7
3

1

2

3

1

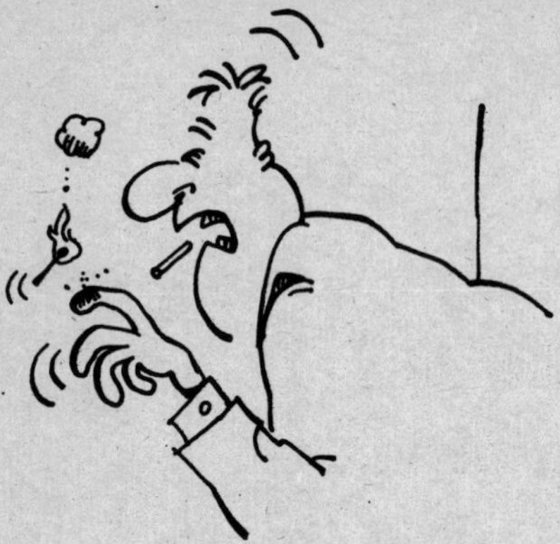

2

PIRANHA

(1)

②

1

2

3

1

2
CURB
YOUR
DOG

SALVATION ARMY

3

MAIL

①

(2)

JOE'S
DINETTE
LAROUSSE
GASTRONOMIQUE

1

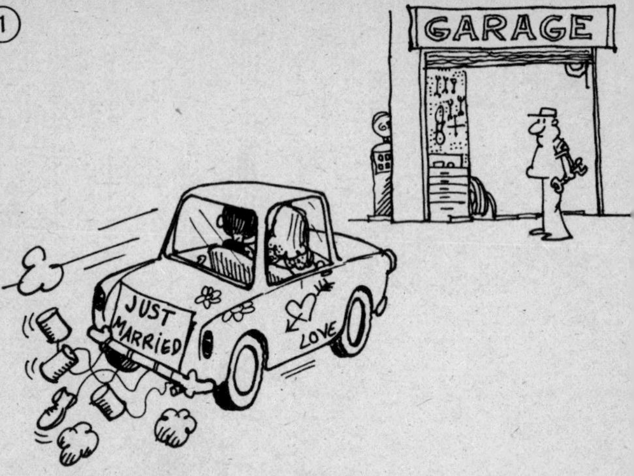
GARAGE
JUST MARRIED
LOVE

2

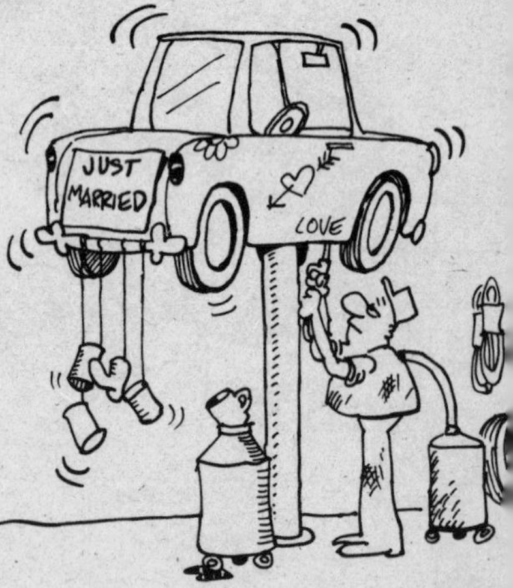
JUST MARRIED
LOVE

3

1

2

1

2

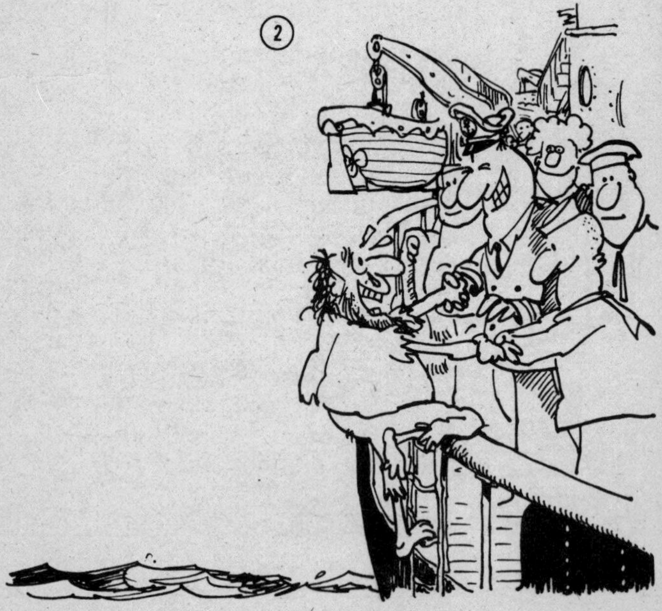

3

1
2

3

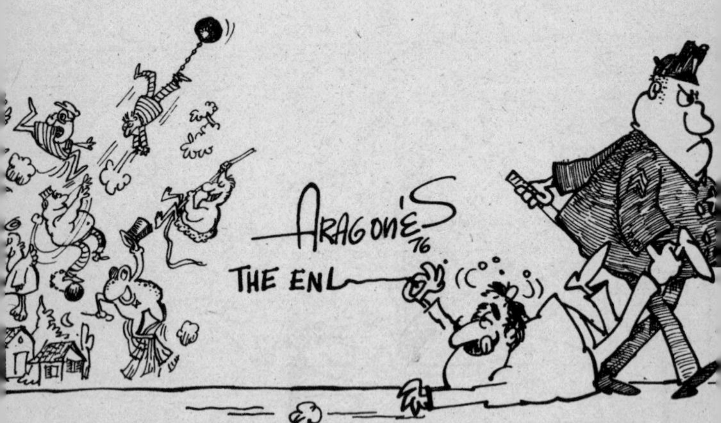
ARAGONÉS 76
THE END